ALIEN TRIBES

WRITTEN
BY
STEPHEN R.
BISSETTE

ILLUSTRATED
BY
DAVID
DORMAN

First published in Great Britain in 1996 by Boxtree Limited,
Broadwall House, 21 Broadwall, London, SE1 9PL

™ and © 1996 Twentieth Century Fox Film Corporation.
All rights reserved.
Cover painting and Tribes logo design by David Dorman

First published in 1992 in the United States of America by Dark
Horse Comics, Inc.

10 9 8 7 6 5 4 3 2 1

ISBN 0 7522 0295 2

Printed and bound in Great Britain by
Cambus Litho Ltd, East Kilbride.

A CIP catalogue entry for this book is available from the
British Library.

ALIENS™
TRIBES

A L I E N S

*To Nancy, Maia, and my son Daniel, and to my father and
brother, Richard and Richard Jr., warriors.*

Steve

*For my parents, Phyllis and John, who gave me something
I can never return in full...time.*

Dave

Acknowledgments

Thanks to Rick Veitch, Neil Gaiman, Steve Perry, Phil Nutman for advice on close-
quarters bodily harm, friends and associates in the Horror Writers of America,
Mitch Berger; to the originators: Dan O'Bannon,
Ron Shusett, Walter Hill, Ridley Scott, H.R. Giger, James Cameron, and
Stan Winston; to Karen Berger and Alan Moore, for putting me on the writer's path;
to Mark Nelson and Mark Verheiden, 'cuz; and to Mike, Dave, Randy, and Barbara
for trusting me on this one.

Steve Bissette

I would like to thank the people who helped me realize the characters in this book:
Lurene Haines, Philip Burnett, Del Stone, Jr., Corky Mitchell,
Kris Lagerloef, Eric Jenrich, and Michael Stoy.
I would also like to thank the people whose help was instrumental in
completing this project: Mark Nelson, Scott Hampton, Lurene Haines, and Dave Elliott,
for their valuable input; Brian Stelfreeze, for legwork; and Ridley Scott,
H.R. Giger, and James Cameron, for laying the Alien design groundwork.
And lastly, thanks to Jerry Prosser for riding shotgun, Barb Kesel for her patience and
indispensable help, and Mike Richardson for
bringing this project to me.

Dave Dorman

A L I E N S

"Protect and Proliferate: That is the Need of the Swarm that we may Serve, the Only Need we Must Serve.

"For Her and Her Own have enemies who are many; for all that is mere flesh Trembles in Her Shadow; and flesh wishes to destroy Her and Hers, lest She humble them and make of their flesh Her own: as Veal, as Vessel, as Cyst or Cistern, to Proliferate.

"The Need we May Serve is as Vessel for The Proliferation; that Need may be Served by any flesh. Serve that Need if you must, if She or Hers so choose.

"Our Call is of a greater Need; know this: we are the Chosen, and so we do Choose: our only Value to the Queen Mother and her Swarm, to Her and Hers, is as i have Written: 'Protect and Proliferate.'"

—The Rev. Dr. Thomas Engstrom
Totem of The Queen Mother
(Banned by Corporate Governor's decree)

A L I E N S

The Queen is dead.

The message raced through the hive with chemical-fueled urgency. A shimmering river of soldiers poured through flaming corridors, double-jaws shrieking with outrage and despair.

The Queen is dead.

Still, the workers tended Her body and cradled Her head, caressing its seared beryl armor, an army of lovers comforting, coaxing whatever spark of maternal love She might still contain. They uselessly tried to knead eggs from Her ruined abdomen, though it was no longer pulsing, no longer suspended, now distended, shapeless, near liquid.

The unborn that slithered from Her shivered in the debris, seeping into the scorched resins beneath Her. The drones wailed their loss, their grief, and ground their argent teeth in agony, and still more of them came.

Their black, mewling mass skittered into the seared rubble of the royal chamber. Multi-fingered hands fumbled with all that remained of the young, unborn Queens, as if they could somehow be pieced back together out of the smoldering indigo remains.

But they were dead, all dead, ripped from the warm, nurturing bodies of the soft ones and split asunder.

The Queens were dead.

The Queen is dead.

Moments after the message had been encoded and spread, the hive joined her for all eternity.

The Queen, the Queens, the hive, and the metal ship they had made their own splashed fire in the void of space. Soundlessly, the explosion blossomed and then imploded, closing in on itself.

There was no debris, no clue that it had ever existed once the implosion had winked shut.

Purged and extinguished, the hive was no more.

The monitors flickered, replaying the incident for 'Bort. The tape began again: the waste disposal pod opening, the alien erupting from it, the blazing gunfire. This is what had brought his squad here to TodLab LXI.

Stop. Rewind. He could not help it; the incident stirred the memories. 'Bort closed his eyes, and replayed his own internal tape:

Even now it mesmerized him.

A quivering under the furrowed translucence of the object. Four rippling lips, blossoming, inviting, a wet shimmer of veined and coiled life hidden within.

The eruption, the shriek, the cold, suffocating dampness over his head. The violation, pulsing into his mouth and throat, his choking spasms only forcing the obscene spiralling further down into his vitals. Then, nothing — nothing until he awakened to a dim, red agony.

He opened his eyes, thick with crust, lids barely responding. A circle of faces, masked, hovering above blue gowns tinged with dewdrops of red. He was bucking, rasping, throwing his head forward to glimpse his belly as it distended impossibly.

A tear in the skin splashed open. A mottled azure mass leaped from the scarlet fount. He felt his legs numb as his spine twisted. The doctors were on it in seconds, a lethal metallic device plunging into the mass.

A spray of citrine pus, burning, steaming —

'Bort opened his eyes and let the monitor display rivet his attention anew. Here were sharp lines and clean readout, the schematically perfect abstractions of the state-of-the-art medical station TodLab LXI, scanned and analyzed as he orbited its equator even now.

Orderly, inorganic reality was all he need attend to now. What was past was past, save for the loss. The legs he no longer had or could truly feel tingled for a moment, just long enough for him to miss them.

Then they were gone, as they would always be. The pang was too familiar and hardly worth a flinch. 'Bort's eyes returned to the monitor as it replayed the opening of the lethal TodLab LXI medical waste disposal pod.

The pod had been methodically taken aboard, its hospital identification symbol recorded, the military staff ready to cope with whatever lay within: all a matter of routine. Hundreds had been impounded, recorded, and opened with clockwork precision by the corporate-funded waste-retrieval and research subdivision, dedicated to the systematic seizure and inspection of unregulated medical waste disposal.

It was a nasty job under the best of conditions, opening the hermetically sealed canisters of medical waste and inspecting the contents. Some of the waste pods were larger than a one-man vehicle, most of them much smaller. All of them took time to inspect. It was a tedious, unpleasant routine. Most were uneventfully brimming with bagged and labeled tissues, organs, and limbs, a cold soup of discarded human fragments peppered with glistening shards and strands of disposable medical technologies. Though the vacuum of airless space ensured their preservation, the pockets of tainted air and random cultures of infectious bacteria always made combing the wastes interesting.

There was an urgency to the operation that belied its routine. And there, in the seven-hundred-and-forty-fourth unit, a discolored pod dumped from a medium-sized medical installation designated as TodLab LXI, the caution proved justified.

'Bort savored it again, the inevitable keying of the senses as the pod was unsealed. At that second of disinterment, all eyes and instruments were tuned, all hands at the ready, all weapons brought to bear on the suspect vessel. Then came the movement from inside, the talons, tail, and teeth erupting, the blaze of pulsefire as the alien spilled out of the pod.

'Bort looked up from the monitors to gaze out of the command module's viewport. He tried to lose himself in the expanse of space, but there was no awe in it for him. Only space, dead air. If men had ventured into space to move nearer to God, they had failed; the void consecrated the emptiness of 'Bort's existence. The only gods men seemed to still worship in this vacuum were aliens like that in the waste pod: offal-eating blasphemies to be scoured and hunted down like vermin.

The hunt, and his omniscient role as overseer, slaked his thirst for bringing the alien hostiles a measure of the torment they had given him. Every raid would arouse him, though he was impotent; each explosion sent a shudder of pleasure up his shattered spine; every hive purged made his truncated flesh less of a prison.

'Bort turned the command module about to face the dark side of TodLab LXI. His eyes followed Tunnel Rat's progress as she moved over the TodLab, its surface bristling with spires and antennae, punctuated by sealed exits and entrances.

'Bort stabbed at the keyboard before him and brought Rat into clear, magnified view on the primary monitor screen. She cradled the implosion unit gingerly, weaving weightlessly like a trout between the obstacles in her path. The unit was the last of four, the other three already positioned and locked into place on TodLab's exterior.

Together, the four units were the mission's fail-safe device, its sensors alert to the presence of the alien hostiles. Once programmed and set to work, nothing could stop it as long as alien hostiles remained in range. If any were detected leaving the station, the device would automatically trigger its own countdown and detonation: an all-engulfing implosion.

If they failed, they would still succeed. The implosion would exert its inexorable force, pulling any and all objects into its wake: inward, collapsing forever inward, until it was spent.

The alien spore would *not* spread from TodLab LXI.

They were hardly gods; they were a scourge, and 'Bort the exterminator.

As Rat cleared a battered airlock entrance iris, metal upon metal folded in a circular pattern, 'Bort broke the silence.

"Command mod 'Bort: freeze it there, Rat," he spoke into his throat microphone.

As always, she refused to reply; she simply acted.

"It's the prime ventilation shaft just ahead of you," 'Bort continued, "those airlock pressure doors. Lock that ticker in place to detonate into the shaft, then climb back aboard."

Again, she acted. She never spoke to him.

Once she had, once —
— *before* —

Rat moved with customary assurance and grace. 'Bort envied that most of all about her: even in her absurd tunnel gear, she moved like a cat. And now, in zero gravity, hugging a "Baby Boomer" — the key implosion charge, three and a half feet of griddled steel — she carried herself with uncanny skill.

It made him ache to watch her. If things had been different, he might have been skirting the abyss with her now. He had been a handsome cadet, once, when he enjoyed the nickname Sparky instead of 'Bort. At that time she did give him the time of day. Perhaps Rat had once loved him, even. He could have been with her today, known her intimately, sharing the insular grunt talk, private asides, and afterwards...

Afterwards she rolled over, her back to him, forever to him. The scars were too deep, and the touch of a man could only echo her father's touch. Her father: the dead man who climbed into bed with them every time they tentatively made love —

A dull knot flared in his throat as his eyes kissed the next monitor.

'Bort gazed at his own image, and as ever he loathed it. Face immobile, scarred, and partially paralyzed. His body was a calloused tube steak squeezed into an armored mobile unit of life-support systems — stomach, kidneys, intestines of plastic and wire a-whirring and gurgling like clockwork. Its chrome surface was broken only by the extension of his right arm. He was no longer a man. The vermin's seed had twisted his flesh and seared his spirit. No man could be his friend, no woman his lover ever again.

'Bort applied pressure with his right palm, and his console responded. Eight screens flickered new imagery: faces, figures. His eyes flicked away from his own hateful visage, shifting his attentions back to Rat: the Baby Boomer was in place, programming console open, her gloved hands punching in the sequential coding, moments from synchronization of the detonation timer.

He looked to another monitor, where a dark-eyed man, half his head shorn of skin or hair and gleaming with scrimshaw circuitry, tipped into view. His gaze met 'Bort's, and without pause he spoke.

"This room won't suffice, Commander," the voice complained. "They say it's the only area under security at this time, and Dr. Cotlow is still refusing to cooperate. No one here seems to know where he is."

"This idea of corporate high security, it's all bullshit, Ears," 'Bort whispered. "They're all bureaucrats, all ineffectual. They don't know what they're doing."

Ears' static-obscured face in the upper left monitor, his voice in 'Bort's ear: "Affirmative, sir. They know why we're here, yo?"

"They do," 'Bort rasped. "I told you, Ears. They don't know what they're doing. How the hell they going to know what *we're* doing? You *take* what you need, and pronto. I want that communication link in place by fifteen hundred hours, and link with Point established."

The facial circuitry twinkled. "Yo. That's an affirmative."

"Point, report."

Point's monitor showed a communication beacon, made in Ears' image, set akimbo on a hospital corridor floor. Point's hands came into view and set

the simulacrum upright, and an impertinent tap of his boot sent its circuitry alight.

"Point, report."

"TodLab sector seven, corridor sixteen-A: beacon set. That makes fifteen. All units responsive, all plugged into the security surveillance systems within the station. You can monitor every corridor. Ears or no Ears, you'll be in contact with all squad members save the Rat at all times. Check."

"That's a check, Point. Proceed to position once Rat's back inside."

'Bort's eyes shifted to the exterior monitor as Rat was coming in, the metallic iris dilating shut behind her. The screen blinked, switching to an interior view.

Rat was inside the airlock, already stripping off her airtight suit, her strangely proportioned battle gear visible in the open locker next to her.

'Bort braced himself, and paused. His eyes lingered.

— *her back to him* —

Rat geared up quickly, efficiently. With the final piece of equipment in place, she shifted her weight and moved towards the open floor-level ventilation shaft as Point's shadow moved across her. Now she looked ungainly, her equipment sculpted around her lower back and hips in an insane parody of the female figure. The gear was sleek and compact, but its positioning looked uncomfortable. Standing was clearly an effort.

As she tipped forward to adjust her knee padding, the gear slid back into advancement position. Suddenly she held the figure of a wasp, poised to fly, venom within. Her flame thrower nestled against her shoulder with easy familiarity.

Despite the high-technology gear, Rat's surveillance system was next to useless. Once she entered the tunnels, visibility in the darkness and signal penetration were dubious at best; she preferred it that way, he knew —

— *the dead man between them* —

Point stepped into view beside her, grinning. "Tunnel Rat in position, chastity belt in place. Keeps the hostiles' pointy peckerheads at bay."

'Bort winced. Point didn't know, couldn't know.

"Okay, Rat, move out and station yourself at the junction of airlocks four-four-niner and four-four-niner-H; await Leader's command."

She didn't reply. She'd never reply.

Rat's body cocked into position, the clumsiness suddenly gone.

As she arched down and into the tunnel, the design of her equipment became apparent: streamlined for maximum mobility in crouching and crawling positions, leaving the arms and legs unencumbered. She was supple and lithe, slithering effortlessly into the conduit, a hornet invading an enemy hive — and was gone.

"Point, get yourself into position: your current sector, corridor twenty-two-C, one click away."

"Affirmative."

"Jiminy, you in?" Point asked.

Ears responded promptly, "I'm in, Point. Go, man, go."

"Keep my conscience clear, Jiminy," Point whispered.

Point's monitor blurred with renewed movement, as he hustled off to

take the high ground. Point's face rarely appeared on 'Bort's screens. He and Rat were the only two specialists who relied strictly on the POV — Point of View — monitoring system: state-of-the-art surveillance equipment affording maximum visibility laced their armor and uniforms, microfilament video and audio sensors threading them with an external nervous system that Ears and 'Bort were tuned into at every second.

Where Rat's monitors were barely adequate, Point's were of the highest resolution. He was the squadron's eyes, and aside from the tunnels, wherever they had to go, he went first. If Point didn't see it, it didn't matter; if he did, and it was alive, it was dead by the time the next in line reached his position.

Point was the man.

"Leader, all mobile units in position. 'Kicker in chains?"

'Bort squinted to focus on the monitor as Leader's features coalesced into view.

"Give us a minute," Leader barked, his bony features tense and already beaded with sweat. "Still adjusting his sedative dosage. We don't want him waking up until we're good and ready for him."

"Settle down," 'Bort fired back. "You've got minimum five minutes, and still no sign of Richards. You'll have all the action you want soon enough."

"We're a fucking kamikaze unit," Leader growled, "and still no token Jap. Let me know when that chickenshit Richards shows."

She spoke without speaking, heard without hearing. The soldiers were essentially deaf to each other. The Queen was the ear, voice, heart, and soul of the hive. They lived on Her every whim, moved on Her every urge.

They were Her hands, legs, and jaws, and they already numbered in the hundreds. Her reach, Her speed, Her bite extended over every niche of this metallic maze they had made their own.

For now, She kept them close to Her, and kept Her own counsel. They strained to catch a whisper of Her thoughts in Her sweat and excretions, but there was none there, for She wished it so.

They tended Her and Her spew with intimate care. As Her lovely glaucous mass rippled with new life, their doubled thumbs closed tenderly over the new spawn. The royal chamber was the hub of a great wheel of tunnels, gleaming networks of resin and chitin bonded with plastic and steel, adorned with the soft ones whose bodies cupped and nurtured the hive's larvae. The eggs were carefully positioned in front of the hosts, the soldiers fixing them into place with their own resinous secretions.

Some of the soft ones had yet to be fertilized. They were cocooned into the walls and wailing, moaning for the kiss of the newborn, their songs shrill and monotonous. Others stood tranquil, their faces masked by the grip of the newborn, the eggs cooled and empty at their feet.

Others showed their chalky faces, now still and blessed with the stirrings of the larvae in their loins, the dried husk of the discarded newborn's shells at their feet. Within these soft ones the growth of the hive lay coiled and assured.

Still others were hidden elsewhere. These were the Special Ones. They would go elsewhere and spawn their own hives.

Occasionally, a soldier would rest from its labors long enough to gaze upon its own host, now greying and putrid in its station on the wall. The soldier's face could betray no emotion; what fond memories did it hold for the soft one who had been its womb? Once fair and warm and freely giving of its fluids, now tattered and cold and desiccated, melting into the bony resins of the cocoon — it seemed the way of all the soft ones, once they had served their purpose.

For a moment, there was no directive in its actions as it lifted its bony talons to the dried face, its touch oddly loving. Blackened, glistening claws tenderly traced the features of this once vital and nurturing husk. The opposed thumbs traced the sightless brow, searching the empty sockets for answers. Then the call of the hive reasserted itself, and the soldier returned to Her needs. As the soft ones served, so would others, no matter that they were frail. There were many, and the hive had use for them all.

She could not see all this, but She knew it was so and knew it was good. She lifted Her majestic cowl, allowing Her milky jaws to settle from their ebony shielding. She stretched them wide, teeth glowering in the muggy darkness, tongue extended in a yawn. She regained Her composure, retracting Her features, bowing Her saurian crown.

A controlled shudder coursed across Her cyanic torso, and its dewy secretions carried Her voice. She spoke without speaking, and whispered softly to the hive:

They are here.

The seductive, computer-generated feminine voice calmly announced, "Lieutenant Tsuruku Richards docking."

Leader's lip curled contemptuously as he muttered, "The gang's all here."

The message was repeated, without inflection or emphasis, as Leader returned to the supervision of Shitkicker's sedation.

'Kicker lay suspended in a network of chains and life-support tubing, locked into two tons of fully armed and armored exoskeleton. The ExoWarrior's monicker had been earned in battle: prior to action, he was simply MOX 16, the sixteenth Mobile Offensive ExoWarrior produced by military intelligence for effective confrontation with the hostile alien life forms. When a civilian consultant, en route from the seminal military skirmish with the hostile organisms on the Terraformer LB 426 Colony, successfully dispatched an alien Queen with an Exoskeletor Payloader, military designers had responded with MOX.

Leader paused to assess MOX Shitkicker's firepower, checking the flame thrower and electroprod of the left arm, the capacity of the new rapid-fire munitions welded onto the right arm. Up, under, and outside, 45mm self-

ALIENS

pumping grenade launchers housed the central Pulse rifles packing 25mm explosive-tip caseless shells, laced with oxidizing chemicals to neutralize the alien organism's concentrated acid blood. The metal sheathing of the recently installed launchers and pulse rifles was unblemished, seamlessly joined with battle-scarred metal plating over the arm, pitted with the last battle's spray of acidic blood.

'Kicker and fifteen experimental ExoWarrior infantry units were the first of their kind. The military wanted a new breed of warrior, and the marines provided them: volunteer basket cases and psychos eager to taste power in this lifetime.

The Berserkers.

It was up to medical science to keep them leashed until they were needed.

The young hospital staff member assisting attended only to the equipment. Leader gazed at the fellow and then peered down into 'Kicker's helmet. Were those his eyes seething between the three contoured view slits in the faceplate?

Could he *still* be awake?

Leader's eyes fixed on the metabolism recorders, coaxing the intravenous sedative intake until the readouts indicated an even respiratory rate coupled with no REMs: Rapid Eye Movements. The chemicals administered to 'Kicker kept him in oblivion — a perfectly modulated, dreamless coma state.

Leader stared down at the MOX faceplate again. This time, nothing glowered beneath the trio of gashes in the faceplate.

"Beddy-bye, Shitkicker," Leader whispered paternally.

The drug slithered through the color-coded I.V. tubing, threading like an external circulatory system through the steel-reinforced armor plating and into 'Kicker's veins. The hospital staffer also checked its progress.

"Isn't he under deeply enough?" the doctor asked.

"Can't ever keep a MOX down too far," Leader countered. "If he starts dreaming, no telling what he'll do when the adrenaline kicks in. You keep a *close* watch on him, boy. Watch those monitors, and watch his eyes —"

The aide nervously shifted his gaze to Shitkicker's cold, unyielding mask.

"— when the siren sounds, you'd best *hustle* your ass out. This wine is going to turn to lava," Leader said, tapping the stimulus I.V. feed, "and this volcano's going to *blow.*"

"But to keep a man in this state for too long —"

"Listen, egghead," Leader fired, "MOX lives and breathes zip, you got me? 'Kicker's psycho-ward one, and this was his own choice of duty. When the bughunt reaches critical mass, we wheel him in, turn him on with a triple dose of chemical adrenalines, and turn him loose. The bugs *will* go down.

"Your job," he monotoned as he jabbed his finger into the doctor's chest, "is to see our MOX stays under, stays blank, and is where we need him when we need him. Then get *out* of his way.

"You keep this sedative juicing. If you register any REM, that means he's dreaming."

Leader whispered through a rictus grin, "Last time one of you circle-

18

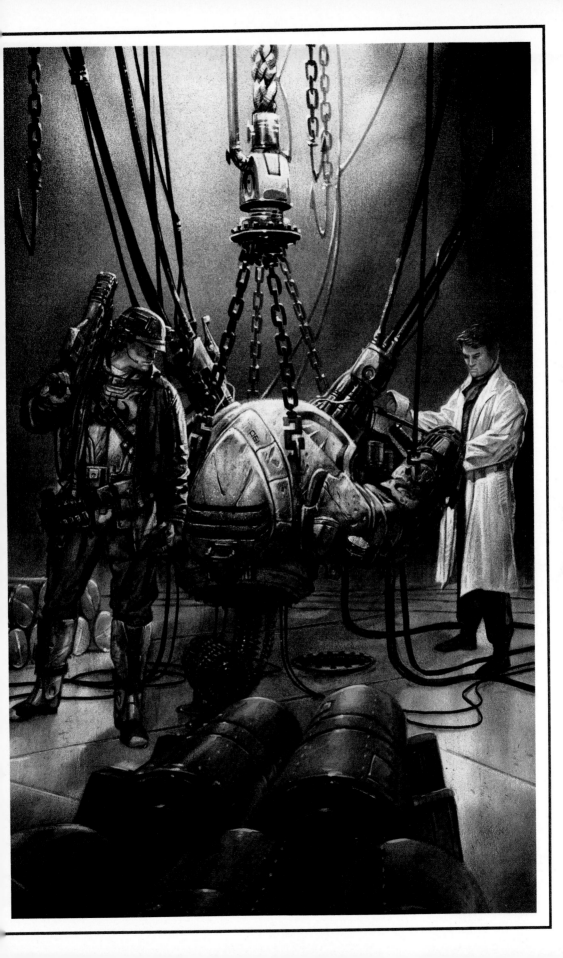

jerkers slacked off with this particular MOX, he had himself a little dream. When it was time for the kickapoo joy juice to wake Lazarus, the candyass didn't have *time* to clear the warpath. Blew the fuckin' nitwit to kingdom come. Accidental death, y'understand."

The doctor blanched, lips drawn tight.

"Sleep with the dead, MOX," Leader whispered. His flinty eyes stayed with the biochemical readout until he was satisfied. He reached out to touch the craters and rivulets that marred the faceplate. The resistant plastic shielding was in place this time. The last battle nearly cost Shitkicker his eyes.

The last battle. One they had survived.

Leader closed his eyes and fought the tremor that churned in his spine. It always hit him prior to the synchronization with the implosion detonator: this might truly be their last battle. The tremor overtook him for a second, locking his knees and steeling his teeth.

It was a moment he shared with no one. He opened his eyes to see the doctor's own stealing away, furtively. If he saw, he said nothing.

"Lieutenant Tsuruku Richards has cleared security," the intercom calmly announced.

Leader spun on his heels and made his way to the reception area.

Lt. Tsuruku Richards' manner was firm.

"I want Dr. Cotlow here, and I want him here *now*," the lithe Oriental sternly insisted. "He is the executive in charge of this installation, and his presence is crucial at this stage."

Tsuruku met the nurse's glare.

"Lt. Richards, we've been unable to locate Dr. Cotlow for almost forty-eight hours," Nurse Jaffry said. "We —"

"That is a lie, Nurse. The hospital's classified log records that he sealed himself into the time-locked pharmaceuticals storage safe only twenty-six hours ago," Richards replied, rubbing his brow. "That lock opens automatically every twenty-four hours. Surely Dr. Cotlow has been freed by now?"

Nurse Jaffry was unable to make eye contact and nervously cleared her throat.

"If you know where he is, miss," Ears suggested, "you'd best get him here."

She shot a glance at Ears, a look intended to wither, but Ears just cocked his head and winked his false eye at her, like an electroplated rooster.

"Nurse Jaffry," Richards added, "tell Dr. Cotlow I resent the repeated alteration of the classification code. It was a feeble attempt. If he is a coward, so be it, but his actions are most suspicious, given the situation."

She replied without turning to face either Richards or Ears. "You don't know what it's been like, gentlemen. The doctor's sector was picked clean by those — those —"

"Yes, forty-six hours ago!" Richards spat. "Why didn't he vacate that

sector and relocate at that time?"

"Husssssstle," Ears whispered.

Her heels clattered down the corridor, their staccato interrupted only as she skirted Leader's approach.

'Bort's voice stabbed over the intercom. "Leader, Ears, Richards. Welcome, Richards. It's about time. Ready to commence final Baby Boomer automatic arming sequence."

Ears wheeled himself into the center of the communications spread. "Affirmative, Commander. We have all in view."

Richards leaned back. This was none of his concern; he was a consultant, the alien life form specialist. Leader glared resentfully: Richards was military-employed, but he was a free agent. An expert in alien physiology, habits, and habitat, Lt. Tsuruku Richards was shuttled from colony to colony, station to station as his services were required. He arrived in his own ship, supervised his own investigations in his own time, and remained a noncombatant free to go once the Queen was destroyed. The squad had to remain, working against the clock to do the cleanup work. Good men died while Richards left in search of another bughunt.

Leader wondered how the man slept at night.

Richards returned Leader's glare, an enigmatic humor dancing over his own. Leader scowled and darted around him, stationing himself over Ears' right shoulder to supervise.

"P.D.T. check," 'Bort ordered.

Ears scanned the smaller screens mounted over the key personnel monitors, each showing the individuals' vital life signs.

One, however, remained blank.

"Personal Data Transmitters for all personnel, check — wait a moment —"

Ears tilted his head back to stare at Richards. Richards sighed and triggered a wristband he wore above his watch; the squad's P.D.T.s were surgically implanted, but Richards was a guest, not a grunt. He wore a portable P.D.T. unit.

The blank screen blinked on, displaying Richards' vital statistics and color-coded vital signs.

"Yo, that's total affirmative."

"Position check," 'Bort commanded.

Ears scanned the larger screens.

Rat hunkered in the airlock junction, a gleaming weave of alien resins carpeting the floor beneath her betraying her proximity to the hive. The next screen shared Point's view from his station. Ears flicked a switch, and both Rat and Point brought their wrist communicators and timers into view.

Leader's face was reflected in the screen projecting his image; Richards, infuriatingly bemused; 'Bort, swollen face lit by his own bank of surveillance screens, eyes greased with shards of geometric lunacy; and last but not least, MOX Shitkicker, vital signs near flatline.

Another battery of monitors was mounted overhead, fifteen in all: the simulacra of Ears' head, positioned to scan prime locations in the hospital, their access to the hospital security system giving them each a thousand eyes with

which to see. One showed Nurse Jaffry, marching back into view, alone.

"All positions, affirmative."

'Bort narrowed his eyes. "On my mark."

Ears glanced down at his own wrist-timer, as the monitors all showed the same action, all timers the center of attention.

"Ten...nine...eight..."

Jaffry stepped in briskly. With a single move, without taking his eye from his own timer, Richards stopped her dead in her tracks by clapping his free hand over her mouth.

"...six...five...four...three...two...one...

"Mark."

"All timers synchronized: seven hours, fifty-nine minutes, fifty-eight seconds, and counting," Ears confirmed.

"You now have less than eight hours to complete the bughunt," 'Bort intoned. "If we fail, the detonator will do our job for us. The infestation must not be permitted to move beyond our parameters. We are all expendable to that end. If we succeed, we will resynchronize and terminate the fail-safe countdown, disarming the device. Then we can pack up, disengage the Baby Boomers, and go home.

"If, however, its sensors register a surviving hostile alien life form, it will remain locked to detonate until that life form is terminated. Each of you has the power to detonate the fail-safe unit from your wristband, should the success of the mission require such extreme action. Be sure, people, if you do. The last thing to pass through your mind will be your asshole.

"Rat, phase one depends on you, as always. You will all take orders from Leader.

"Good hunting," 'Bort concluded, shifting out of view.

The three men in the communications center turned to face Nurse Jaffry, her face twisted with confusion and indignation.

"The doctor will see you now," she stammered.

Leader bolted to her and grabbed her arm.

"Let's *go*, Richards!" he barked, dragging the nurse in tow. Richards gave a parting glance at Ears and followed.

Ears turned his full attention to the monitors. Point's moves were decisive, calculated, while Rat moved furtively into darkness. She made a clicking sound — her signal to Ears that it would be audio communication only for a time — and Ears programmed her monitor to display a grid of the airlock system, a single flashing light indicating her position within it.

Rat stopped and moved her head to the side, trying to catch the sound ahead.

There was no point in trying to get a visual fix on it. It was too dark, and Rat trusted her hearing above all. Once, her ears had been tuned by autumn breezes between leaves and the plaintive cries of twilight birds (*and father's footsteps, coming up the hallway, keeping the lights out so that mommy wouldn't see*), but that had been long, long ago and far away.

Now, her world was a labyrinth of metal, oil, and the resinous sheathing that inevitably led her to the heart of the hive.

The sound was a soft, rhythmic patter moving toward her, growing softer as it rippled over the cancerous resin carpeting the aliens habitually left in their wake. Whatever it was, it was not a hostile. This was tiny, and Ears hadn't given the signal to indicate approaching danger. She reached down to touch the hardened secretions laid over the conduit flooring. There was no moisture here. She was still a safe distance from any current alien activity.

With no threat at hand, she brought the infrared viewers down into position and looked towards the rhythmic shuffling. She rarely used the viewers, as the urge to see distorted her own sonar. The darkness — her strength, her shroud, her ally, even against (*daddy*) the aliens — honed that sonar, and was a comfort to her.

Her patience was rewarded with a glimpse of a thin, tubular creature as it cleared a bony structure of resin. It briefly waved feathery tendrils in the darkness before coiling itself into a crevice in the ribbed nadir of the deck. As it did so, something was pushed out of place, something with fingers: the husk of an alien newborn, its spidery legs like bony talons curled uselessly around the withered sac of its spent body.

Rat prodded its thorax, but it was brittle: at least a month dead.

Cautiously, she looked up at the walls. The cocoon was still in place, but it was empty, its human host gone. The chrysalis had been broken open, the body that had served as womb mysteriously absent.

They *always* left the husk. It ceased to matter once they shed it. Rat scanned the interior cavity: no tissue, no blood. The host had been removed with care.

What took the body? She had never known the aliens to touch the husks after the gestation was complete; even the newborns did not regard the discarded flesh as food.

Rat looked down and away, bringing her eyes to rest on the coiled little being that slept nestled amid the skeletal knots of resin. A soft, reassuring undulation seemed to begin at the coil. It was soothing, swelling in nearly tangible waves from the creature's rhythmic breathing. Rat lifted the viewers and let her ears take over again. As the darkness embraced her, the sounds sharpened.

Yes, she was sure of it: the creature was *purring*.

The darkness became a screen, and Rat savored the image the creature's purring conjured. A kitten, dimly remembered, its name forgotten, but the aftertaste of her love for it briefly rekindled. Its green eyes had been trusting, gray fur soft and yielding — (*no daddy not my kitty!*) — and then darkness reasserted itself.

As she ground her heel to proceed forward, something slithered underfoot. Rat shifted her weight, and it wriggled free, a soft skittering that dimly echoed behind her.

She waited until the sound had passed, and moved on.

Doctor Piers Cotlow's eyes were pools of indifference glimmering in sallow features as cool and blank as the unbroken wall behind him. They betrayed no concern, no malice, no passion. There was no hint that he cared at all about Leader or Richards, or what they had to say.

Leader slammed his fist onto the desk, spilling the good Doctor's coffee. "Goddammit, I want some answers, Cotlow!"

Cotlow didn't even blink. "Anger is counterproductive, Sergeant," he cooed with dry amusement.

"Richards, I've got a battle to attend to," Leader spat as he faced Cotlow again. "*Your* fucking battle, Doctor! In seven and a half hours, your battlefield could be less than atoms! Do you know what a four-way cross implosion does to a shitball tub like this?"

Leader slammed his fist into his palm and ground it, his face fixed in a grimace. He didn't wait for a response, he simply turned to Richards — "You get *answers*!" — and marched out of Cotlow's makeshift office.

Cotlow's reptilian gaze remained undisturbed. He watched Leader strut down the corridor, then turned to Richards.

"How can I be of help, Lieutenant?"

Point's monitor shimmered with nightmares.

"Point, talk to me," Ears whispered.

Point whispered, "You gettin' this, Jiminy?" as he entered the operating theatre. According to hospital records, this was the last site occupied by the hostile organisms. Tracing the hive from the last known point of action was always the simplest route for Point, leaving Rat to trace the air ducts and ventilation system according to Lt. Richards' projections.

Ears shuddered. Surgery held a special horror for him, but whatever had happened here went beyond the butchery Ears had endured at the military's orders.

An operation had been in progress. It was apparent no one had entered since the attack. The footprints that splashed and spread the puddles of blood all bolted *away* from the body. The operating table was corrugated with acid burns, the tile floor puckered and burned through by its corrosive spatter.

The patient's body — what was left of it — was strewn in gristle, pulped from the core of a moist cavern in the abdomen, ruptured from within. The distended torso bent impossibly, twisting the head away from view, its face buried in the wet pillow as if to stifle a shriek.

Against one wall, a surgeon was splayed, neck akimbo, eyes milky, his skull shattered from above.

Point grunted. Despite the obscuring knot of clotted hair, the serrated edge breaking the flesh of the surgeon's forehead identified the wound,

indicating the depth of the initial strike of the inner jaws.

The kiss, the alien's distinctive bite.

Point hunkered down to get a good look at what the surgeon held in his stiffened hand. Something ribbed, organic, a sac with coagulated rivulets of a flavescent ooze frozen between the surgeon's gloved fingers.

"The walls, Point, what's that on the walls?" Ears begged.

The monitor wavered, and then focused on the room's walls. Four bodies hung there, but gravity had no pull on their extremities.

"They were torn out of their cocoons and brought here," Point croaked. He studied the wizened, long dead faces, mouths agape with unheard screams. Their breast bones split outward; they were spent hosts. The fourth was obscured by still-glistening resins and a dangling jungle of I.V. leading into his — her? — mouth. The liquid stilled in the I.V.s was yellow and cloudy, the color of the tawny slime in the dead surgeon's grasp.

Point looked down, and Ears followed the movement.

The host was dead; the seed in its chest had been torn free, the corrosive burns that defined the wound indicating the nature of the attacker.

"What were these doctors *doing* in here, Jiminy?" Point wheezed.

"Take one more look around, and move. There's enough here to show Richards; maybe he'll know."

"Affirmative. Don't let this get you down," Point said.

Point was Ears' man, the only member of the squad who gave a damn about him. The others didn't trust him, he knew that; Ears was as close as military regulations allowed to a synthetic. He was a cyborg, a fusion of flesh and circuitry, designed as the optimum mobile communications unit. To the others, though, he was close enough to the hated androids of military history horror tales.

"Wish upon a star, Jiminy," Point whispered.

"Dr. Cotlow, you talk of cooperation, but you remain evasive," Richards asserted. "You've responded to none of the military or corporate directives. Have you any adequate explanation for what was found in the TodLab waste disposal pod?"

Cotlow folded his hands on his desk, unperturbed. "The result of a successful attempt to terminate the infestation. The remains were disposed of properly."

"A *live* drone and *sixty-four* newborn alien husks?"

"We made our report to the corporation."

"Yes, *after* notice of the pod retrieval. You *knew* there was an infestation, but still failed to report it."

Cotlow sat back, looking down at his own hands. "You know the history of disastrous military intervention, Lieutenant. We did not want you people involved. Our own security force dealt with the problem."

Richards leaned forward. "Doctor, you are under military and

corporation-enforced quarantine and martial law. You did not quell the infestation. Your records do not add up.

"You were previously among the staff of MatteiLab XX, which also suffered an infestation requiring military intervention."

"Yes, but my tenure was brief and ended long before the military intrusion," Cotlow reflected. "As I recall, your marines ultimately destroyed the entire station, including personnel and patients."

"The investigation revealed that MatteiLab authorities had deliberately kept the infestation secret from both corporate and military intelligence. Incomplete and altered hospital records indicate a careful monitoring of the proliferation and activity of the hostiles, with select hospital environments carefully prepared for alien occupancy. One transcript even hinted at possible use of select patients as hosts for alien progeny."

Cotlow's voice came with an edge now, "Lt. Richards, I lost patients, staff, and associates in our attempt to deal with the problem *here*. All our records are in disarray, much to our own distress. There is no Machiavellian scheme here, no hidden agenda. Do your job, and we will get on with ours."

"We still have the patients who were not evacuated before your arrival, due to your stringent security measures, including an infant in our maternity ward who cannot be moved under any circumstances."

"Are you a religious man, Doctor?"

"Are you, Lieutenant?" Cotlow returned.

"I've scrutinized your files. Your degrees in medicine are accompanied by honors in the higher philosophies; your treatises indicate an almost passionate search for possibilities that terrestrial, corporate-sanctioned religions seem incapable of providing. Since then you've deliberately avoided any discussion or debate on issues other than cold medical science and practice. The question of religion becomes conspicuous by its very absence."

"Matters of faith no longer concern me. The musings of fantasists have no place in administrating an installation such as this," he replied, folding his hands as if to cup the whole of the TodLab facility.

Cotlow rose, but Richards stepped between the desk and the door. "Why did you lock yourself into the pharmaceuticals safe for a full day, hours after the organisms had made their presence felt in that area?"

"An accident, nothing more."

Richards stepped aside. "I have the tapes. We shall see."

"Religious contraband was also found aboard MatteiLab XX, affiliated with an unsanctioned cult reportedly deifying the hostile alien life forms. As an ex-theology student, what is your view on such a self-destructive religion?"

"If you consider my incident in the safe as an act of cowardice, so be it. I am a civilian corporate executive, beyond the reach of military punishment for imagined transgressions. Good day."

"I'll be watching you, Doctor."

"And I shall be watching you, Lieutenant."

Cotlow snapped up a file on his desk and curtly pushed past Richards.

"This is better than sex, lovebirds," Leader's voice crackled over the headset. "Time to grease some crawlers. I'm proceeding down shaft sixteen-A to seventeen-C. Point's found alien entrance to their last reported atrocity, and it's a cakewalk to the hive.

"Rat reports an open airlock at six-niner-eight-G, no apparent cause. She's closing in on Richards' projected hive site upon my order. Lock your viewscreens down —"

Leader flipped his own goggles down over his eyes.

A preprogrammed map of the airlock and floor plan flared into view, a grid pattern overlaying the corridor he was about to hustle down. He shook his head to snap into it: the sense of dislocation gave, and his training asserted itself.

"Lock and load, move it out," Leader ordered. "I'll be moving in behind you once we get Shitkicker in position."

"Where is this room?" Richards asked.

"Operating theatre, here," Ears replied, pointing out its position on the grid map. "Point has already moved on. Looks like your guess was right: he and Rat are closing in on the same position, this engineering sector."

"What were they doing with these bodies?" Richards whispered to himself. "Clearly, they were studying the gestation period, but what" — he tapped the monitor screen, the image paused on the I.V.-riddled cocoon — "were they up to?"

Leader's voice cut the reverie. "Richards, report."

"Watch yourselves, Sergeant. This resembles aspects of the MatteiLab XX incident too closely. I think our team of doctors was engaging in some inappropriate research. Any sign of the hostiles yet?"

Ears interjected, "Negative, sir."

"On your toes, Sergeant. Be as wary of the staff here as you are of the aliens."

"Affirmative, out."

Richards' eyes had never left the monitor. He brought his finger up to the dead surgeon's hand, rapping the screen softly.

"Give me as sharp a color printout of this section as you can, Ears," he coolly proffered. "This — this is significant. Order one of Cotlow's staff to enter and retrieve a sample of this substance from the operating theatre. I'll need a clear monitor to study the tapes from the pharmaceutical safe when you get a chance."

Rat sat in the dim light, staring across the open airlock. The sound of activity at the far end of the duct — perhaps a quarter of a mile away — kept her stationary.

Suddenly the light from the corridor below flickered.

"Shhht! Leader," she cautioned.

Rat looked over the rim of the opening. Leader had indeed heard her. "They're ahead of us," she whispered, "close enough to hear our radios. On my own now, on your orders."

"Affirmative, so ordered," Leader whispered. "How you stomach them taking you, I'll never know."

"No different than any man," she replied, looking away.

Leader shook his head. He glanced down the corridor, toward the hive's probable location. His Steadiflex rocked into his shoulder as he glanced up at Rat, tipping his right hand to his brow.

Rat did likewise, and Leader was gone, stealthily moving back well out of hearing of the hostiles. He would be back for her soon enough to snatch her from the jaws of hell.

Rat inspected the airlock. Unbroken, running between the opened floor of the conduit and the ceiling of the corridor, were a pair of heating pipes. She tentatively touched them, biting her lip (*"not a peep from you, little girl"*) so as not to make a sound. They were hot — very hot.

Steam, perhaps, or heated chemicals, better yet.

Rat reached behind her and freed a loop of hairwire filament from her belt. She methodically unwound the loop, all the while stealing glances down the duct, where the wet sounds of movement continued without interruption.

"Ahead of you, Point," Ears reported, "200 yards, two hostiles, with a war party beyond them."

"Yo, Jiminy."

Point flattened against the wall, flicking the booster on his pulse rifle. Virgin action, about to lose its cherry.

"Sit tight. All move on Rat's signal."

"Set to private comm, and tell me a story, Jiminy."

Point heard the click, and then Ears' voice caressed him like honey, now soft and melodic, his and his alone.

"Yea, though I walk through the valley of death, I will fear no evil..."

The file fell and scattered over the floor. The shakes overtook Cotlow

as he sealed the door to his office. The spasm started in his gut, threatening a grand mal seizure unless he contained it.

He fumbled for the bottle in his coat pocket. Frantically, he tore the cap loose and shook out a handful of pills, gulping them all down. They were bitter, but the rush of bile up his throat was worse.

And then the craving for the jelly — it was all he could do to swallow.

Cotlow rolled his sleeve down and studied his arm. The straps were tight enough to bite into his skin, which was already beginning to discolor from the effects of the overdosing. He bent his elbow, feeling the sliding of the needle as the motion nudged it deeper into his vein.

No matter. It was barely visible under the folds of cloth. If he were careful, even the Lieutenant wouldn't take note of it.

Cotlow ran his tongue over his teeth. The sweet residue of the jelly was fading, already a memory.

The X-rays were positioned over the light table. The dark mass in the abdomen had grown. It was nearly full-term. All was well; if only he could maintain this pace and keep Her dormant for another seventeen hours, all would be well.

Nurse Jaffry's voice broke the silence. "Dr. Cotlow, the analysis of the final list of patients has been completed. They are cleared for military deboarding procedures."

Cotlow rubbed the back of his neck, his fingers checking the filament that creased his hairline and fed miniscule dosages of another nervous system control reagent into his system. The touch urged another rush into his cortex. He shivered at the jolt, struggling to maintain his composure.

"Yes, well, continue, Jaffry. What of the nursery?"

"The McCormick infant remains. Should we —"

"He cannot be moved at this time, Nurse. I've wired the appropriate information to the authorities."

"Sir, the military —"

Cotlow flickered perceptibly, his eyes locked with hers.

"See to it," he hissed. "I'm not to be interrupted for the next fifteen minutes." He cut off the reply even as it came and lost interest in her before she had moved to go.

The X-rays were still of interest, but he could not maintain his concentration. His eyes were focusing correctly, no telltale dilation; the lenses and eyedrops would stabilize any indication of his real state. But there was no correcting the inner eye, stoned on synthesized opiates, stimulants, and the blessed jelly. Cotlow massaged his temples and tipped his head back, to the side, forward. Maintain. Protect. The imperative asserted itself.

In the blue light of the X-rays, his face seemed touched by their — Her — immaculate light. His skin glowed with azure perfection, basking in the sensation, cobalt eyes unblinkingly fixed on the dark fetal shape in the abdomen that lay exposed before him. After a final study, Cotlow snapped the X-rays down one by one, tucking them under his arm.

When the light board was cleared, he carried the films over to the waste disposal chute and unceremoniously dumped them. Cotlow coiled out of the room.

In the darkness, the X-rays spun leisurely down. They reflected the dim light like slippery, weightless mirrors.

Softly, they settled upon the mass of papers, tissues, emptied pharmaceutical blister packs, and dry debris. A new strata was added to the station's disposable history, riddled with Cotlow's fingerprints.

Rat lay back in the shaft, admiring her handiwork. The wires were strung at intervals, pulled taut and laced like a cat's cradle across the expanse of the entire conduit's opening. The cord was acid-resistant, but the aliens' blood would nevertheless dissolve it after it had done a little damage and slowed them down.

They'd have time to realize she wouldn't struggle, time to decide to handle her with some care. After all, she would be of use (*"don't tell mommy"*) to them.

She began to tap her foot rhythmically. That would do the trick; they'd be sure to come soon.

Rat listened as Ears quoted the Bible. Her father used to read from a bible, but it was like no bible she'd ever seen before or since. It frightened her, then and now. It had put her brother in his grave; she tried to picture him, but could only remember his body lying in the cot, a flower of blood and bone bursting from his chest, the seed's faceless face rearing up from his rib cage.

Her father's bible had killed her brother and condemned her to this tomb.

Not like Ears' bible at all. She liked to listen to Ears read, even if it was meant for Point. She was eavesdropping, but it didn't matter. All she could do now was sit tight and wait, tapping her foot.

She would let them (*daddy*) take her. She wouldn't fight (*"that's my girl"*) so that they'd take her deeper into the hive.

Rat brought her hand down to her hip, touching the beacon unit locked into her gear's shielding. She would turn it on when they came for her: blow the whistle, and Shitkicker would come running.

They needed her. She was the linchpin, the key to the success of the bughunt. She tapped the beacon and listened as the sounds in the corridor (*daddy coming*) moved toward her.

She closed her eyes as it happened: the wet padding of their veined feet. The squealing (*daddy*) as they struggled with the webbing, the soft hiss of acid blood, the wires breaking as they burned through. The moist sounds and their clammy touch (*"that's daddy's girl"*), thumb over thumb, as they took her, carrying her deep into the hive…

'Bort flinched at the report: "She's in."

His eyes fixed on the dim motion of sleek, tubular forms, giving way to spines and armor, ebony double-thumbed claws closing over white flesh.

He closed his eyes, as always.

They had her.

"She's in," Ears reported.

Lt. Richards stood behind him, watching the monitor as the eerie procession played across the screen. One alien kept rearing into view, as if to peer out of the monitor, while the others secreted the resins, thick and glistening, over Rat's body.

"Fascinating process," Richards muttered. "How does she stand it? I've never seen anything like it in any other team. She's in a self-imposed trance state, brain rhythms slowed, respiration down, heartbeat even, while those creatures do *this* —"

"Her father taught her everything," Ears drawled.

"Eastern meditation?"

"No, sexual abuse. He was a pedophile with a passion for the bug Goddess. Religious fanatic, like those crazy bastards on board MatteiLab. Sacrificed his son, like some self-proclaimed Abraham, to those things —"

Ears paused, rubbing his eyes.

"Rat can shut herself right down...her way of coping, I reckon."

"Fascinating, the way you're *using* her," Richards responded, hypnotized by the dance of chitin, veins, resin, and flesh.

"She volunteered, like the rest of us. They've positioned her *here*," Ears interjected, pointing to the gridmap display.

Richards studied the patterns intently. "Quite close to the royal chamber, I'd say. Are the sensors and counters set on her hip gear?"

Ears flicked a switch, and a readout was superimposed over the monitor screen, obscuring Rat's cocooned torso. The numbers ticked off, ever descending. "Affirmative."

Leader's voice crackled. "Get into position to *move*, people. 'Kicker is in position. Keep Rat onscreen — you've got to get me to her, Ears. Richards, what about that operating room?"

Richards brought a tiny television monitor up into position, tapping the screen with his middle finger. "Get this onscreen for Leader," he ordered.

"These are breeding experiments. The alien life forms were nurtured, and this —" an arrow appeared indicating the rope of yellow syrup flowing from the dead surgeon's fingers "— is most ominous. It is a substance used to generate Queen embryos. A 'royal jelly,' if you will. It is a synthetic."

Leader's voice hissed, "They fucking *made* it here?"

"I'm sure of it."

Cotlow hovered over the nursery bedding, admiring the child. His eyes

were flat, cold blades amid the false winks and smiles.

This is where the new hive will be born, when the time comes. The new Queen would choose this innocent. Cotlow mustered another smile. This one was genuine.

"Dr. Cotlow."

Cotlow turned on his heel, his face slate once more.

It was Richards, accompanied by Nurse Jaffry. Cotlow leveled his eyes at her, transfixing her. "My orders —"

"Your orders are meaningless now, Doctor. Have you forgotten that you are under martial law? I have already transmitted the hospital records to military command."

"Nurse Jaffry —"

"You may go," Richards told her. "The Doctor and I must talk."

Nurse Jaffry nervously looked to Cotlow, who also nodded. Relieved, she bustled out of the nursery.

"You can end the charade, Doctor. We've discovered the breeding experiments. Why would you wish to breed a Queen?"

Richards watched the furtive gesture to the back of the neck, the momentary flush over Cotlow's face.

"It took the corporation two decades, three colonies, and many lives to realize the folly of nurturing these creatures," Richards raged. "They are of no use. They are too uncontrollable. Did you think you could prove otherwise?"

Cotlow rubbed his neck again. The stroke forced another dose of opiate into his veins, and he began to laugh.

"Prove *what*? I don't have to prove *anything*, Lieutenant."

"You *idiot*," Richards flared, slamming Cotlow back with the heel of his hand. The push triggered a dose of stimulant, and Cotlow's mood shifted to sudden anger. He jerked his head back, eyes wild. Richards eyed him warily. The infant began to cry.

"Your folly was to have dreamed you could *control* the implacable will of Her creatures," Cotlow retorted. "*Your* people brought them here. Your executives, you, I, we are mere vessels of divine providence, molding human clay to provide a medium for the fecundity of the Messiahs. They are pure predators, Lieutenant. There is beauty and justice in that. None of you *sees* the truth —"

Richards' face reddened. "Beauty? Justice? You sanctioned these operations! To use these *patients*, stimulate the birth of new Queens —"

"'To Protect and Proliferate,' Lieutenant."

Richards recognized the passage from the MatteiLab contraband.

"You are devoted to these beings, these —"

"And you hate them. You might as well hate the stars. They are elemental beings, and as such, closer to Divinity. Of course the corporations failed; we cannot impose our feeble abstractions upon their primal truth —"

"My God," Richards muttered.

"You and your paternalistic *God* are *nothing* in Her shadow. You and your God are the insects —"

"Cotlow, it ends here. You know that."

Cotlow put his hand to his stomach, reverently.

"It won't. I am Chosen."

Richards paused, stunned, his eyes moving from Cotlow's down to the doctor's belly, harboring alien seed.

"You can't — they wouldn't — how can you still function?"

Cotlow slipped back his left sleeve, revealing the intravenous feed. "Over twenty hours alone in the safe, long enough to allow impregnation, to awaken, to prepare for and prolong the gestation process. I've made her into a Queen as well —"

"The jelly —"

Cotlow smiled warmly, his words flowing like honey. "Of my own invention, Lieutenant."

Cotlow moved toward Richards with mantis-like quickness, scalpel in hand. Richards responded, pulling his right hip back; the flat of his right palm thrust forward with a snap of the hip, punching into Cotlow's sternum. It was a death blow, pulled with a calculated precision to interrupt rather than stop the beating of Cotlow's heart.

The effect was devastating. Lethal shock dropped Cotlow as Richards spun around him, maneuvering all his weight onto his left leg to thrust his right foot into the kidney. The side kick should have demolished the organ, but Cotlow's hidden stimulant canister caught the blow, the impact pressuring feedlines into his spine. Cotlow was jolted by the megadose, the rush: not the reaction Richards expected. He stepped back, realizing his error. Cotlow's temples bulged and eyes glowered violet as he turned on Richards with inhuman speed.

Richards cocked his hip; a left palm thrust intended to promptly burst the heart was broken by Cotlow's spidery countermove.

Richards' neck snapped in Cotlow's hands.

The infant bellowed louder, panicked at the sudden tinge of death.

Rat slowly allowed herself to surface. Layer by layer, she awakened into her body (*daddy is gone*), now held tight by the resinous cocoon in which the drones had encased her.

Across from her, another cocoon: a man, his face hidden by the smothering grip of the newborn, quietly forcing its seed down into his throat.

Rat gasped, and looked down. An egg lay before her, its pink cruciform lips wet — as yet, still closed. She struggled to move her hands. It was no good, she was bound (*no daddy*) by the secretions. She wriggled her wrist and felt the heft of her pulse rifle, still in its holster. They hadn't tampered with the gear this time.

Her fingers stretched, seeking. A click, and then another, from her belt. The sensors were functional. The timer was activated.

She had sixty seconds.

Cotlow dragged Richards' body to the far end of the nursery. He was too stoned to easily recall the airlock's combination, and his kidney hurt terribly despite the painkillers: Richards had inflicted grievous internal damage. A squeeze of the tubing at his neck brought lucidity; now, if only he could work his fingers properly.

The Queen kicked in his abdomen. He doubled over, coughing blood. Another dose of sedatives and she calmed enough for him to finish his task.

Stenciled overhead was the warning: "DANGER: WASTE DISPOSAL CONTAINMENT." Cotlow punched into the second combination, opening the lock. His ears felt the shift in pressure as the disposal unit's airlock yawned open in the bowels of the station.

He savored the ease with which he could lift the dead man's weight, despite his own injuries. Cradling the broken throat, he easily slid Richards' feet into the opening, savoring the ludicrous expression contorting the Oriental's features.

Just as Richards' body was in position, Nurse Jaffry walked in. Cotlow dumped the Lieutenant's body into the unit, and hurried after the nurse.

The soft hissing of the opened unit remained after the clicking of heels, the pounding of fists, and the sobbing had stopped.

Rat squeezed her eyes shut.

The pulpy lips of the egg throbbed, as if engorged and ready to burst with its unholy fruit.

The countdown ended.

A high-pitched whine sounded, and the charge in her hip gear exploded, shattering the resin cocoon. By the time the drones responded to the concussion, Rat was free.

The homing device flashed its signal in the command module, and 'Bort let go of the pain. He curtly checked Leader's — her savior's— position.

"Ready and able," Leader responded, "let the good times roll."

With a Cheshire grin, 'Bort leaned back to see Shitkicker's prone figure suddenly trembling; he was the midwife, watching Hell give birth and break loose.

Rat's detonator echoed through the hive, mobilizing the alien workers to intercept the intruder and protect their Queen.

A corresponding explosion was taking place between MOX 16's ears. First, a dull pressure, barely perceived by the somnambulist. The valves regulating the flow of sedatives seized shut. The exoskeleton hummed with new activity as an array of pumps and valves came to life, flushing newly synthesized chemicals into the comatose warrior's circulatory system.

Adrenaline, fiery and vital, poured into his veins. Flesh swelled against its fetters, its sweat a hot dew within its sheathing. Veins distended, thick with molten fury.

Before his eyes snapped opened, the self-pumping grenade launchers had begun to spin as the pulse rifle built and tested its own charge.

His eyes bulged as the second dosage was booted, sparking crystalline urgency. The restraining chains rattled, stretched, broke.

Shitkicker bolted erect, flexing his lethal arm extensions, stamping his legs like a bull. A scanner dropped before his right eye, flashing a grid map of the installation, a flashing marker indicating his primary objective. A path charted the maze of corridors to be negotiated.

The third megadose of adrenaline tore through him. It was not flesh that trembled; it was steel. Blood and steel. Orbs blazed in their pounding sockets, glaring out of the three gashes carved into his faceplate.

MOX 16 — Mars, the Bringer of War — had awakened.

Shitkicker shuddered and launched himself forward, arms loaded and ready.

"I'm in," Leader ordered. "I'm getting Rat out of here. Check those viewscreens, and stay out of 'Kicker's path of entry."

Leader's pulse rifle was leveled, intent on potential targets. He crisscrossed to the next entry, resins cracking under his boots.

"Hostiles, closing on you," Ears reported.

The first dropped from the wall, unfurling itself from the resinous layering. It moved soundlessly, tail and talons crooked to strike.

Leader peppered it with rapid-fire bolts. It shattered, an ochre blur flecked with sapphire. Four, five, six more rose in its place, like some crustaceous hydra.

He continued to fire into the horde of aliens, their dark fingers flexing even as their streamlined heads and bristling torsos exploded into corrosive mists. The metal of the corridor walls and floor cratered, buckled, and flowed, magma chrome tinged with yellow.

Leader hustled forward, head cocking from side to side, responding to every flex of chitin and bony hide.

A tail would flash, scorpion-like, from above: a burst would vaporize the attacker. Another tarred scorpion sprang from the crevices of the hive walls; a succession of rapid-fire bolts split it, and its brethren, into pulp.

In their wake, a tawny mist of sulphur and brimstone rose, pitting the walls with its acidic kiss.

'Kicker surged forward, legs pumping with piston ferocity. Loaded cylinders spun, stopped, tripped, and spun again, restless for their targets.

The objective was still distant on the grid map, a dim flash at the end of the ever-shifting maze.

An urge to shake his head, to clear his thoughts, asserted itself, but the strapping within his helmet restrained any such movement. His view was fixed ahead, only ahead. He flushed with rage, speeding the rush of stimulants in his blood, straining at his leash like a mad dog.

Forward, only forward.

Rat moved along the resinated catwalk. It was narrow, which was a comfort of sorts; when the aliens attacked, they had little room for surprise. Her gridmap indicated the location of the ventilation shaft that would bring deliverance.

She struck another flare, and let it spin to the flooring below. In the lazy drift of its light, a beryl shape clambered into the shifting shadows: another hostile, en route to the royal chamber.

The vermicular form froze, bulbous head alert, coiled, and sprang. As it caught the catwalk grating underfoot, Rat fired into the monster's face. Its crescentiform skull careened back and the alien dropped, bursting like a water balloon far below. Rat struck yet another flare, and let it drop: 'Kicker's one-way trail to the Queen.

The vent shaft was just ahead. Something dark and serpentine slithered into it. Rat brought her rifle up and stopped.

A hiss from below. Another behind.

She heard Ears' warning in her headset: "Hold tight."

The flurry of movement ahead in the shaft entrance was met with the crack of rapid fire. Blue tracers burned through an alien, ruptured into spiny gristle as it.exploded from the vent.

"Hustle your Rat's ass!" Ears barked, and Rat vaulted forward. A venomous tail struck at her side; she barely eluded its lethal blow.

A cobalt rustling from beneath, now scrabbling for a purchase on the catwalk, reaching —

Breathlessly, Rat leaped into the ventilation shaft as Leader strut into view, his pulse rifle already blazing into the monsters behind her as she dove to the flooring. She felt the heat, the ochre haze pitting her arms like hornet stings.

"Move, move!" Leader shouted, as they both bolted down the conduit.

Ears' monitors had proved the success of the mission thus far. No casualties as yet, Rat and Leader moved away from the hive's center, skirting Shitkicker's path. Cleanup would begin soon.

Smooth moves, all the way.

Ears paid special attention to Point, who already waited at home base. It was a rare moment, Point at rest: Ears watched, reached out, and touched the screen.

"Yo, Jiminy," Point whispered. "'Kicker is on his way."

On another monitor stood Leader and Rat, backs to the wall, eyes locked on a passageway lined with cocooned victims.

Leader stared at the cocoons, stony-faced.

Steel rippled underfoot; the wall rumbled at their back. It was Shitkicker, following Rat's flares to the heart of the hive.

Fifteen monitors with compound eyes followed MOX 16's path, consecutively recording the monolith's progress. His movements were perfection, a juggernaut in heat.

'Kicker the unstoppable, picking up momentum with each step.

MOX 16's eyes narrowed as he rounded the bend and spied the entrance to the hive proper, its surfaces sculpted by alien resins. His steps quickened, the wraparound pulse fire extremities clacked and whirled. He rocked forward, the charge of the Berserker, and let loose with the grenades.

Within the unyielding armor, 'Kicker orgasmed. The pump action was invigorating, the fiery concussions intoxicating.

The aliens poured out of the hive, from every nook and cranny, tails and talons extended, and he cut through them mercilessly. The oxidizing agent in the 25mm shells created a fine, bracing haze of sulfuric blood, which weltered and hissed with every burst. MOX sucked the mist into his mouth, giving a flavor to his bloodlust. It burned and numbed his tongue like a drug: the taste of first blood.

The grid's triad in 'Kicker's faceplate was obscured by a blur of cyanic armor: an alien on his head, clawing at the intruder's armor. A second one leaped onto the exoskeleton's back. He bellowed as he brought the electroprod into play, jolting each in turn to the resin floor to be splattered by pulse fire.

Another dose of stimulants pumped into him, and he accelerated towards Rat's flares.

Another indigo wave of drones descended on him in defense of their Queen. There was an uncanny precision to their ranks as they erupted from the ceilings and floors, ebony talons and stingers flashing, but their strategies were ground underfoot and dissolved under fire. They were unable to slow him as he charged, guns and torch blazing, adorned with fountains of ichor.

'Kicker passed Rat's shattered cocoon, the marker's signal triggering another dose of adrenaline. He roared down the passageway in a shower of resinous splinters. Still the creatures tore at him, leaped at him, scrabbled for a handhold on his armor. Jaws gaped at his view slits, the teeth within gnawing

ineffectually. MOX's eyes widened with pleasure as the attackers were demolished with the flick of a finger, the flex of an arm. The juggernaut could not be contained, crashing into the royal chamber's steaming expanse in search of its heart.

'Kicker paused at its perimeter, his blood roiling. He gazed across the rows of freshly laid eggs as the throng of drones moved to surround him.

The Queen stood at the chamber's center, her bloated cerulean body suspended from the interior superstructure by thick, viscous bands of webbing. She turned her head to face him, her cowl flared and jaws distended. Her soldiers slithered beneath and above her, all turning to face the giant intruder who stood rocking in the debris.

Despite their intelligence, their mobilized numbers, they could not save her from the ignoble intruder.

It was over in seconds.

'Kicker roared at her spineless majesty as the grenade launchers pierced her in the throat, thorax, and abdomen with 45mm charges, detonating on impact.

The Queen shuddered and fell. Her nearly severed head veered crazily, jaws akimbo, toothy tongue spewing her death throes. Her vitals slagged wetly into the mire of drones and eggs, the wellspring of the hive imploding into a seething, loathsome caviar.

Shitkicker savored the moment, his head pounding.

The webbing still held her wriggling remains aloft, legs thrashing in staccato agony, until a round of 25mm fire brought it all down.

There was no need to bother with the Queen any longer; he dispassionately turned away. The hive froze, regarding the lethal intruder with cool, calculated awe. The silence may have lingered, had 'Kicker refrained from torching the entire chamber, royal court, fragged Queen, and all.

Their hesitation shattered, the aliens retrenched to move behind him, scurrying to protect the fetal Queens in the closest passageways. 'Kicker chased them like ants, letting them lead him to primary cocoons. As the drones embraced them, or tore the human hosts free of the resins to carry them out of MOX's range, he roared like a lion and brought them all down.

Oily smoke bellowed through the encrusted corridors, and the cries of the tortured hosts fed the flames.

Point had already begun his rounds, tracing the passageways adorned with the cocooned near-dead. He didn't look at their faces. These weren't people any longer, they were hosts, bodies locked in resins, exposed faces ash-white. The precious eggs — some yawning cavities, spent and empty, others still harboring their seed, awaiting the delivery of needed hosts — lay positioned at their feet.

There were no salvageable ones: all were infected. Most were unconscious, mercifully comatose as they nurtured the gestating invertebrates.

Some were awake — praying, moaning, sobbing at their fate, gibbering for deliverance.

Point delivered them all.

Cleanup detail.

'Bort watched Leader and Rat proceed with the same grisly ritual. They began closest to the hive, killing creature and living host as they spiraled outward. Eventually they cleared the hallways and begin to scour the vents and conduits, destroying those hidden away without pattern.

Leader did so with methodical precision. Rat moved slowly, leaving the children for him to deal with. By torch, by pulse rifle, by blade, they all were terminated, human womb and fetal monster, together or separately.

The cleanup ended in streams of blood, acid, and bile. Streams converged into rivers, seeking the crevices in the acid-resistant resins, burning their way into the metal flooring, flowing deeper into the heart of the station.

The Queen lay in Her own blood, feebly trying to raise Herself. As She rallied, something gave in Her torn neck, and Her head twisted painfully. Her devoted minions could not help Her; they, too, had been butchered and scattered by the giant.

Her spindly legs managed to gain a foothold, and She tried to lift Herself up out of the steaming coils of Her own insides. Her legs stayed firm, but what was left of Her body splayed open and apart. Her once regal cowl spilled back into Her savaged torso.

Though Her head was demolished, She could still hear.

The gleaming giant was still destroying Her chamber. This giant spat death for the hive.

Unless the young Queen survived.

She had sensed its presence of late. Until now, the knowledge of another Queen growing within a soft one — one mysteriously able to move about outside of the hive, capable of functioning even as the larva matured within it — had been a threat to Her.

A threat to Her was a threat to the hive. But She had refrained from its destruction, choosing to bide Her time.

Now it was the hive's salvation.

Her ruined head could not move, but Her lips slid back, Her jaws shuddered open, the sweat broke upon Her, and She spoke without speaking for the final time.

The hive froze in response and listened.

Save Her, She sang without singing, save the new Queen, for She is your only hope.

The hive swayed as one, as the new call was heard and repeated, the

ALIENS

taste of the new Queen retained.
The Queen is dead.
Save the Queen.

"Jiminy, I don't like this."

Ears kept his eyes from the monitor. "I know, I know — they're massing as if to move —"

"They're usually on us like ugly on an ape...but no sign of 'em," Point worried.

"Point's right," Leader affirmed, "something is amiss. The hostiles aren't trying to tear us apart while we're aborting fetal Queens. What the hell? *Now* we need Richards, and the sonuvabitch has flown!"

"Negative," 'Bort's voice interjected. "Richards is still aboard."

Ears stared at Richard's P.D.T. Flat. Dead.

"Then get him front and center — we *need* his useless ass!" Leader shouted.

"The bugs are moving *around* 'Kicker," Ears blurted out. "One flank moving as a group, the others breaking into groups fanning around in the same direction."

"*Richards*! What's the score?" Leader cried.

"Destination apparent?" 'Bort interrupted.

"Sector one-niner-oh," Ears calculated.

"The fucking nursery," Leader shouted, "*Richards*?!"

Ears looked imploringly at 'Bort's visage on the screen.

"Richards is dead," 'Bort replied tersely. "Has been since you began the sweep. You read me?"

Leader bowed his head and spat.

"You read me, Leader?"

"Cotlow," Leader whispered.

"He's in hiding. Consider him hostile, armed, and dangerous. Ears has already confirmed he killed one of his own staff outside the nursery shortly after Richards' death."

"Point, to the nursery. Rat, it's you and me into the vents," Leader said. "We make way to Point, but cover all the ground you can between here and there. No telling where those last Queen bees might be.

"Consider any hospital staff an enemy.

"Hustle, grunts!" he ordered.

Ears checked Richards' P.D.T. readout again. Flatline.

"Finally of use to us, and it's no show," he murmured.

Rat and Leader were making good time until they found the cocooned boy, mouth agape and reddened eyes staring. The emptied egg at his feet told

the tale. Rat froze (*daddy, what did you do to brother?*) as Leader approached the child. He looked so much like her brother —

"Jesus, he's still alive," Leader winced, reaching behind his back to unsheathe his blade.

Rat lurched forward (*no daddy!*), but it was over: the death rattle was barely audible. Blood splashed from the boy's chest, a wriggling within. Leader fired into the slender rib cage. He shook his head, fighting the wave of revulsion, and whispered, "Come on, Rat, I need you with me."

Rat stared at the boy's still face. Her agony was punctuated by Ears' warning.

"Two hostiles, doubling back into your proximity!"

Though shaken, Rat rallied. She instinctively cocked her head, trying to locate the soft, insidious movement from above.

"— more moving into range, 100 yards behind you —"

Rat spotted the tear in the conduit wall ahead of them. The first alien slid in with alarming grace and speed, despite its size. It reared to its full height, arms spread like an angel of death, pausing as its obsidian companions climbed down behind it.

Rat tipped her muzzle up and fired. She was still dazed, putting her first shot off, shattering the alien's knee. The impact sent it reeling, but its tail snapped into lethal play, lashing Rat across the chest and slapping her down.

Leader rushed into position beside her, rifle blazing. Rat heard him shout something as she righted herself. One of the creatures plunged onto him, and they spun out of view through the ruptured wall. She heard them crash below, Leader's shout swallowed by gunfire.

Rat tore a length of wire out of her hip gear and leaped onto the alien closest to her. Despite its angry thrashing, she held long enough to lock her knees around its midsection, straddling it as she twisted the wire around the pearly girth of its head.

Rat pulled the line taut and let herself fall back. The monster fell with her, hissing. It raged to right itself as Rat tied the wire to secured piping, the rapid motion sinking the wire through her worn gloves and into her palm. Resisting the pain, she made sure it was tight before rolling clear. The hellish thing shot its arm towards her.

Rat came to her feet as the alien clawed at the wire. She swung her rifle down off her shoulder, pausing only to be certain of its load. Gauging the distance to the opening Leader had vanished into, she made the leap.

The alien dove forward to have her. The wire held, closing over the creature's canescent flesh and cutting deep.

Still it thrashed forward. The noose closed completely, severing the back of its head in a dappled spurt. The wire glowered and dissolved in the spray of acidic blood, but it had done its work. The alien's tail coiled over the wound spastically, its jaws wide in the death scream.

Before Rat could reach the opening, the other was on her. Its talons had her head, thumb locked over thumb. Its lips peeled back (*no daddy*), baring the jaws, silver and beckoning (*don't kiss me*). The inner jaws darted from between the rivulets of chrome saliva and teeth. Rat rammed her rifle up into the lower jaw, severing the protruding tongue as it sank into her cheekbone.

The monster bolted back in pain. Rat went with it, the inner jaws tearing free of her face, her head strangely clear. As they hit the conduit flooring, she slammed the rifle into its jaws again. Droplets of acid sprayed over her like venomous dew, riddling her torn face and chest with spongy dots of fire.

The alien was lost in its own agony, its hands closed over its leaking maw. Rat hobbled up onto her knees, using her rifle as a support. As she did so, the alien's tail lashed out, smashing her into the wall like a rag doll.

It caught her, opening its ruined jaws as if to strike. Rat twisted free, the talons tearing skin and uniform. Again, its tail, the stinger biting into Rat's thigh, moving to stab between her legs as she lost her footing —

— and suddenly she was falling, falling away from the monster. Rat braced herself for the moment of impact, but it came with blessed, soft ease, as she landed in the dry garbage hold with a rustling of paper and plastic.

Rat turned to look up at the alien teetering above her. A crimson dew — her blood? — shimmered on its phallic skull. The head moved with the glacial, hypnotic flow of a cobra, but the metallic iris closing above her moved more quickly to seal the waste disposal chamber.

The monster thrust its hands into the dilating closure, as if to force it open, pulling its talons back just as the iris slid shut.

"Gotcha," Ears shouted into her headset.

Rat closed her eyes, drawing in a short, deep breath, opening her lids with the slow exhalation until the air was spent.

"You're in a dry waste disposal chute," Ears said. "I was able to locate and close the airlock above you. Your P.D.T. registers all vital signs stable. You're all right."

Her breathing steadied, slowed.

As it did, her head relaxed against the garbage mattress that had saved her. She let her head tip to the side, her gnawed cheek and torn chest now rich with pain and blood, her pitted chest afire. She brought her free hand up tentatively, running a single finger over the wounds, cautiously trying to assess the damage.

She opened her eyes. The dim light caught what seemed to be a mirror beside her, slick with oil.

"Rat," came a whisper in her ear. "Rat, please reply."

She reached out to touch the object. The motion was comforting: she was alive, despite the pain in her head and the frightening numbness in her leg. Her fingers caught it, the surface cool and slippery, and lifted it out of the debris.

Rat strained to roll over and examine the object. The light from above, however dim, shone through it. It was translucent, a piece of film. She brought her arm around to her torch. Turning it on, she held the film over its glare, recognizing it as an X-ray, showing a male body, a dark, spidery shape within it.

"Rat, we are receiving. Do you hear me?"

A male adult's body, and a mass within — she heard a deeper voice, 'Bort's voice, Ears replying to it, then he was talking to her, his voice strangely tender.

"Rat, what is that on the screen?"

" F-film," she whispered.

She had seen an X-ray like this before, in her father's laboratory, years ago. Her brother — he had planted the seed in her brother —

"Rat, this could be important." Ears replied, "Is there any date or identification visible? Is there a *name* on the X-ray?"

Her eyes brimmed with tears. The type, so small —

"Cot..."

"...Low."

Suddenly the headset sparked with voices. Rat could no longer follow or separate them.

In the distance, a baby wailed.

Leader thrashed across the corridor, away from the alien. It stood in hideous cerulean splendor, midnight visage swollen with rage, externalized ribs distending, before leaping at him again.

He spat rapid-fire bursts into its face, rolling clear of the caustic welter. Its talons tore into his leg momentarily, but could not hold. He bellowed death into it completely, leaving only shattered armor and pulp-cratered flooring.

"Ears," Leader shouted, "talk to me!"

"She's okay," Ears responded, "I saved her ass."

"Repeat, Rat is down, but not out," 'Bort confirmed. "You are to move on, soldier. It's Cotlow —"

"Terminate Dr. Piers Cotlow."

Point crouched in the shadows, listening.

"Take him out," 'Bort ordered, "Dr. Piers Cotlow has the new Queen gestating inside him. Terminate with extreme prejudice."

The identifying image of Cotlow flickered in his viewscreen, along with a grid map flashing his last known location: the nursery.

"All other hospital personnel are expendable. Consider them armed and dangerous. You have one hour, forty-seven minutes before Baby Boomer begins countdown," 'Bort reported. "Status: Richards dead, Rat down, Leader en route to Point's position.

"I'm *all* you've got besides each other, grunts. 'Kicker is A-number-one berserker. Ears will relay relative positions: steer clear, unless told otherwise. P.D.T.s check, and make your way to the following posts: Leader, relocate to sector one-niner-oh, junction of corridors forty-six-D and E; Point will need your back-up."

The hive was ravaged. Metal fuselage and shielding melded with alien extremities, a crazy quilt of organically wed biomechanoid textures and forms. Sanguinary corrosives sparkled and pooled like quicksilver, seeping deeper into the station's internal superstructure —

Shitkicker could not stop. The synthesized adrenaline roared through MOX 16's veins as the flooring supports were eaten away, bending and buckling beneath him. 'Kicker's pulse rifles kicked through the walls, flame throwers torching the cocoons, though they, too, had already been purged.

Suddenly the floor gave way beneath him, and he was sinking into it, tipping off-balance, splashed with debris and pooling acid gore, plunging into the floor below —

Stimulants triggered, testing his arteries.

The fall spun him, his blazing eyes recognizing what lay below. With split-second response, the grid map flashed a schematic of the structure he plunged toward.

A thought: response, before contact.

Grenades fired into the airlock, opening new frontiers.

Point stepped into the hall, careful not to catch himself on the jagged metal. 'Kicker's passing had opened a lot of options, burning and busting through airlocks and doors. Getting into this sector would have taken him another ten minutes without 'Kicker's path cutting up to the hive.

Ears cautioned, "Bogies ahead: six. 'Kicker's shitkicking *above* you: look out for potholes. Nursery ahead via niner-niner-A junction. There's an infant in there, still alive."

"A *baby*?" Point snarled.

"Watch for Cotlow. Leader should be with you in a few. Out."

Point hesitated over the body of a nurse. Her neck was broken, eyes were fogged over. Point could guess how she died.

Cotlow.

He gingerly stepped over her and continued to corridor's end. Two aliens stood guard before the nursery door, bodies folded into porcelain abstraction. Another azure gargoyle perched above the entrance, unmoving save for the quivering of its mottled external veins. There were probably more, hidden in the ductwork. Infrared unveiled the sleeping beauties that stood vigil dangling from the corridor ceiling, limbs and spiny tails woven into the pipes that laced the installation.

Inside the nursery, a baby was crying.

There was music: trumpets, a cacophony.

A voice — a man's voice — was singing.

"Leader, you'll have to intercept 'Kicker," 'Bort commanded.

"No fucking way. He's locked into overdrive, weaving diagonally — coming down through the *roofing*, for Christ's sake!"

"He's cutting through the installation," 'Bort growled. "The aliens seem to be deliberately throwing themselves in his path. Their blood — Ears has a fix on him en route to Point's locale. He'll take Point *and* Rat out unless you can stop him."

"Position," Leader snarled.

Ears knew better than to speak. Leader's viewer grid indicated Point's position. The MOX signal rampaged through the grid, cutting through walls, doors, shafts, and airlocks: a juggernaut aswarm with hostiles, their blood eating the flooring.

And down he would come, Berserker on a rampage.

"Down on my fucking ears," Leader snorted.

"Intercept," 'Bort repeated.

Leader moved, breathing heavily and beginning to roar, as if he could pound through walls as well.

Point drank it all in. Six hostiles: three prone, three up. Point brought his rifle scope up to his eye and watched the replay: the trio of guards at the door, the creatures woven into the fuselage above, probably with back-up.

What were they guarding? This wasn't like any behavior he'd seen before in eleven cleanup operations. Whatever was inside was important to them.

Music, brassy and pulsing, throbbed from within. Something screeching, something crooning.

Point brought his rifle to position, its hydraulic support softly hissing.

An answering hiss came from above.

He didn't take the time to look up and glimpse the creamy jaws, already open to strike: he fired blindly, pulse fire sending it careening. The protective gear caught most of the acid. He hustled into the hallway junction, pulse fire ricocheting off the ceiling fuselage, catching a second hostile up across the abdomen and chest, spilling it into the next burst of fire leveled at the nursery sentries.

An alien spun and splashed against the door, another leaped into point-blank range and took the explosive shells in the face. A third skittered up onto the walls, lunging out of range as the metal sparked behind it. The other remained on the ceiling. Point's fire rippled vertically, keeping it pinned until it was shattered by the barrage.

The next volley caught the wall-climber, creasing its ribs, a torrent of gold corrosive splintering the chitin. The wounded monster rolled impossibly up the wall, prehensile tail coiled, and plunged. Point reared back, slamming the monster against the steaming metal even as it hit him, but it held, arms locked over his chest.

Already he could feel its tail lash toward his vitals. A rope of saliva

slid past his shoulder: its jaws were agape, the inner chrome teeth gasping. Point bellowed and tipped his rifle up into it, blistering his own face as the creature's maw exploded. Fire flowed down his back, and then he was free.

The other alien was not on him yet, coiled to spring once its ruined brother was clear.

Point rolled and fired as the being hung in midair, tipping his arm and rifle over his head as the fountain of ochre fluid splashed over him. The acid steamed into his flesh, his howl drowning out the music and infant cries from the nursery.

"Point!" Ears bellowed.

Leader stepped up his already frantic pace at Ears' scream.

"Point!"

In his haste, he disregarded the warning flash on his viewscreen, his collision course with MOX imminent. The ceiling above him exploded, slamming him to the floor. Slabs of steel and shards of metal rained down as the core of the explosion spent itself overhead.

Leader crawled forward as another bolt ripped into the adjacent wall, detonating into the parallel corridor. He stood to face the piston-driven madman who stepped out of the ruins.

Shitkicker loomed, swollen with bile and rage, the lunatic puppeteer strapped into his monster puppet. 'Kicker stormed ahead, fixed on some unknowable goal, oblivious to the soldier standing before him.

Leader fought the fear and awe that washed over him; MOX was just a grunt, like him, and his orders were to take him down. The exoskeletal sheath rendered the warrior within almost invulnerable to Leader's available firepower: he would have to get *inside*.

'Kicker's stride was enormous. The next step would put him out of reach.

Leader grabbed the reinforced leg struts and found a handhold above the knee. As he pulled himself up, 'Kicker felt the weight, adjusted his balance accordingly, and then slammed through the wall.

The impact nearly tore Leader away from the exoskeleton. As the leg lifted for the next step, Leader used the motion to move onto firmer purchase at the hip, swinging up and around to the ribbed armor-plating on Shitkicker's back.

As the new wall was breached, the ceiling above it suddenly bristled with life.

The hostiles were here, moving en masse.

Rat awoke with a start.

Thunder pounded overhead.

Rat painfully craned her head. Her shoulder hurt terribly; she had twisted it in the fall. And her face, her chest —

"Rat, do you read me?" Ears choked. Despite her painful stupor, she could hear his torment; it roused her further.

"Christ, Rat, get *out* of there! It's all gonna be coming down on *you*! Get *out* —"

She struggled to raise herself up. As she leaned her weight forward, the cushion of garbage beneath her responded. Paper, plastic, cardboard, and debris gave slowly at first, then in terrifying lurches.

Rat tried to lie back, to stop the sickening motion, but it was too late. The displaced waste parted, plunging Rat into its suffocating mass.

Above, the thunder raged closer.

Leader held on for dear life, though the armor's slickness gave little purchase. He looked up as he strained to gain a new handhold on 'Kicker's helmet, his eyes furtively registering the frantic movement of the aliens above.

MOX was four-alarm crazy now. He could feel the weight of the intruder on his back, moving up the ridge of his spine. The machinery responded: megadoses of stimulant pumped anew, the juggernaut raced forward as the torch arm bent back, already raging. The other arm fired another barrage of 25mm explosives.

By the time the torch was clearing 'Kicker's head, he had pounded through another two walls, the squealing aliens seething overhead. They seemed to be gnawing at their own bodies, their corrosive lifeblood pitting the floor beneath them —

The flooring gave way as 'Kicker leaped to the wall, clearing the acid-eaten floor's weakest point. Leader struggled to climb higher, though the acid was pissing through his back. His skull felt raw and blistered as the corrosive gore sprayed onto him.

If he could clear the spine, if the first shot made a dent in the head armor, if —

The world tipped sideways as the flooring collapsed.

The flame thrower lurched backwards over MOX 16's head, and poured the fires of hell onto the gnat on his back.

"I'm all right, Ears!" Point cried, "Get your shit together! We need you, we all need you *now*!"

Point cradled his acid-riddled arm. The burns were deep and painful, but his concern was more for the pulse rifle. Checking the corrosive scoring, he leveled the barrel at the scarred nursery door and fired. The rapid fire was no longer rhythmic. Erratic bolts riveted the door, buckling the metal without piercing.

"Damn!"

"Point —" Ears interrupted, but the attempt was too little, too late.

Point barely had time to back against the wall before the ceiling above split asunder. He rolled and fell hard, almost into the path of the berserker as it crashed into the deck.

'Kicker was a fireball, spitting, shitting, screaming fire in every direction. His right leg corkscrewed with the fall, toppling him through the wall beside him.

Point pulled himself over on his side, every alarm wailing. There was something on 'Kicker —

The battering arm rounded the lip of the crater, sprouting pulse-spitting rifles at the center. Fuselage flared overhead as the shots ripped across and down, pounding the nursery door. Its other arm was bent up and overhead, as if trying to scratch an itch it couldn't reach. MOX's back was aflame, and something was writhing in the blue hell. The torch was suddenly extinguished. The arm's electroprod unit jutted from the barrel, catching the pitiful figure that still clung to the exoskeletal spine full in the face.

The figure stiffened with the jolt and then fell, limp and horribly blackened.

Point saw it all, mouth frozen in a ridiculous grimace, eyes blurred red.

Shitkicker knew none of it. The gnat was off his back, he could focus his ire exclusively on the hostiles, though they were now two floors above him, their blood still intently sprinkling into 'Kicker's path. He whirled with terrifying speed and accuracy, and fired upwards. The creatures began to drop onto his exoskeletal armor, tails stabbing spasmodically.

A monstrous sound of screaming metal resounded as the flooring beneath MOX's two-ton frame began to give. 'Kicker turned and glared at Point, cocking his arms as if to fire before plunging through the weakened floor to the next deck level below. The aliens began to drop down through the crater, out of sight.

Point crawled hand over hand, like a lost child, to the broken and burned body.

"Leader," he whispered, tentatively touching the body.

Point struggled to his feet, letting the wall support him as he struggled toward the open nursery before the monsters turned their attention back to him.

The soft hissing of the open waste disposal airlock was barely audible over the din from the lower deck. He could *feel* it more than hear it as he eased his way into the nursery.

A baby was crying, its howls muffled by the thundering music. At the center of the cacophony was a man, alone.

Point's scope fixed on the man's back. His aim was shaky: the acid burns had cut deep. More than just pain and shock had compromised his strength, as tendons and nerves had been cauterized.

The music swelled, crescendoed, as the man leaned back and waved his arm drunkenly to emphasize the sweep of the symphony. Something was wrong with him. His back peaked in impossible places, as if he had two broken spines. The nape of his neck bristled with shimmering, spaghetti-like knots of tubing splayed against his shoulder blades. His arms seemed distended, preoccupied with erratic scooping motions, a jerky, spasmodic laboring over — what?

With the baby's screaming — where *was* it? — Point couldn't put what he was seeing and hearing together into any coherent picture. The baby's shrieks crescendoed with the music as the man lurched erect and spat blood, the agonized chorus punctuating his pirouette to face Point.

"Stra — vin — sky," the figure stammered.

"Jesus, Point, right behind you," Ears implored over the headset, "do him and *move!*"

"Le S-sssssacre du — Printemps...Rite o-of Ssspring —"

Point brought his eye up from the scope. Even with the damage to his arm, the idiot loomed at point-blank range before him. He couldn't miss. Nor could the scope make sense of the spectacle.

Point had to see this with his own naked eyes.

"Appropriate — d-d-don't you think?"

The man teetered into the light, his eyes glassy and nearly bursting from the sockets. His nose was streaming murky fluids streaked with blood, mouth smeared with something thick and viscous that ran in yellow threads down onto his shirt. All about him was a sickening weave of I.V. tubing from multicolored canisters into gleaming needles, sunken into bloodied cloth, swollen and bruised flesh, into veins and nipples and crotch.

"P-play chess?" the madman slurred. "R-Richards thought he could t-take me, too —"

"Cotlow!" Ears bellowed through the headset, "It's Cotlow!"

"— take my Queen —"

Point's eyes widened as they fixed on the center of the man's chest. His shirt bulged unnaturally. Something was writhing beneath the splattered fabric, something small and wild.

A hissing, louder than that of the open airlock, from behind.

"*Point get out —*"

Another hiss: the hiss within the hiss, wide to strike.

"*PointPointnononogetoutmanoutou —*"

The idiot, Cotlow, clutched to hold the creature that writhed under his shirt, his mouth distended.

"Wish upon a star, Jiminy."

The trigger kissed, once, twice, three times, as Cotlow's temple splashed ruddy snot and bone, his shoulder ruptured in an arc of iridescent chemical-tinged blood —

The alien behind Point struck, its extended tongue tearing effortlessly through the helmet's metal to taste the soft gray yolk that lay under the bone.

Fifteen heads in fifteen corridors: they were the safeguard, the vital link that would be maintained if Ears were killed. Their orbs continued to function properly, feeding visuals and statistics to 'Bort in the command module.

The radio link, however, was inexplicably severed.

Fifteen simulacra irised their mesh jaws wide and bellowed Ears' grief into the very marrow of TodLab LXI's interior, echoing into 'Bort's command module. They were lost now, shorn of their fist and shorn of their brain. Leader and Point dead, Ears was lost: but the monitors unflinchingly recorded it all.

'Bort shut down the link with Ears for the moment.

He had to save Rat — so close, so close.

Only a moment, and she would be safe.

The thunder roared closer, still closer.

Rat lay still until the garbage had finished shifting. She was blind now, her hearing barely functioning; the din from above was too great. Something foul pressed against her lips. All she had was her sense of touch.

The weight of the garbage wasn't overwhelming. She tried to move, to twist her body so that she might crawl ahead. As she shifted her legs, the weight shifted as well, and the sediments of debris parted again.

Rat screamed this time as she plunged deeper into the refuse, the horrible motion abrupt, but quickly over.

"Rat."

She heard his (*Sparky?*) voice.

"Rat, you have to respond."

She tightened her lips, her eyelids.

"Ears can't help you, but I can," 'Bort whispered.

Rat tried to move, but her legs were pinned.

"Rat, you're above an ejectable waste disposal pod. If I can open the airlock, it might be a way —"

Tears squeezed from her closed eyes, and she could no longer hold back (*Sparky, please*) the sobs.

"Can you secure your oxygen reserves?" 'Bort asked.

Rat struggled to free her good arm enough to edge it down, over her thigh, and behind. With each motion, the burden of the refuse that trapped her pressed with renewed urgency. Her ribs, her back ached with every stolen breath.

"Signal me if you can..."

Her hand stretched, fingers burrowing through the trash, until the smooth, unyielding contours of the oxygen tanks defined themselves.

'Bort's (*Sparky's*) voice was strained. "...no more time, it's 'Kicker, the bugs coming down, the acid —"

She pressed her palm against the oxygen reserve and began to cry.

"— *Rat speak up there's no time* —"

She wanted (*sorry*) to say it (*loved you*) so that he would know. The rain became a torrent as the thunder exploded, as the monsters slithered through the waste and reached (*love*) for her (*you*) —

Her ears ruptured as the pressure suddenly gave, and the mass that contained her shifted, plunged, and was swallowed whole.

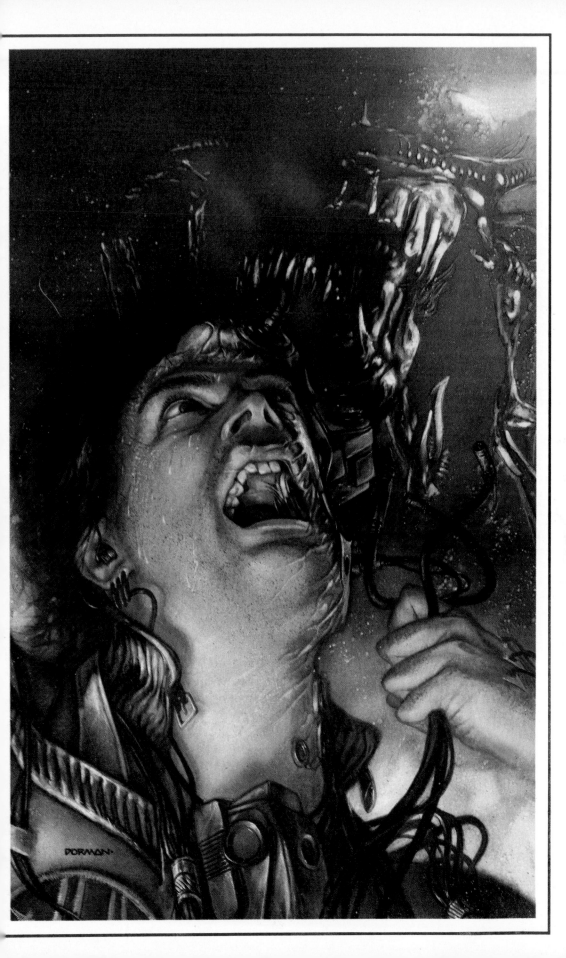

'Bort tried to maintain the tenuous link between himself and Rat. The waste disposal unit had contained her, and she was safe for the moment as Shitkicker plunged through another deck and into the refuse conduit.

"Ears, can you read Rat's vital signs still?" — Ears was screaming, unintelligible now — "*Ears!*"— tearing at his face, his head, shrieking —

'Kicker was still visible, the acid blood washing over him, burning into him as the garbage dissolved and plunged him toward the waste disposal pod.

'Bort ignored the howling and thrashing on Ears' monitor: Ears held by double-thumbed talons, a ribbed bolt plunging into the circuitry of his face —

"Rat —"

She couldn't hear him, as Ears and his many heads howled like the damned.

— on his monitor, Ears transfixed by the lethal tongue —

'Bort cursed, and activated the ejection of the waste disposal unit. He wept as he trusted her to oblivion, watching the tiny silver unit jettison from the base of the station.

Rat was suddenly free of the refuse's burden. For a split second, the din ceased as her ears popped with the extreme pressure change.

In the same instant, the sensation of the nauseating plunge had become that of drifting, dreamlike and dissonant. Her urge was to curl up, like a fetus in the womb, but her fingers maintained their grip on the oxygen reserve tanks.

A new gravity imposed itself as Rat was flung headlong into the void.

The rest were gone, all gone. Rat's screen, ominously black; Leader's mere static. Even Shitkicker was gone, ejected with Rat's pod, his screen exploded with flames, sulfur, garbage, and shattered armor before flickering into midnight. As would they all.

'Bort maintained. Amid the shitstorm, he alone maintained.

All that mattered now was that they had won.

'Bort flicked Point's monitor onto the big screen.

Cotlow was the key: Point had smeared him, just as something — the newborn Queen? — had begun to emerge from his chest.

But it had happened so quickly: he had to be *sure.*

'Bort replayed Point's monitor. Despite the blur of motion and subsequent shuddering, he could see Cotlow thrown back by the impact of the shot to his shoulder. He was hurled back, slamming into something dark that

seemed to collapse — what was it?

'Bort replayed it again: Cotlow lurching into view, something under his shirt. He zoomed in on Cotlow's shirt, where a small, wriggling mass appeared beneath the fabric.

And again: Cotlow's head and shoulder splashing, his body thrown akimbo against a door, the sign overhead.

'Bort froze the image and zoomed in closer. The sign came into focus, reading D-A-N-G-E-R-W-A-S-T-E-D-I-S-P-O —

'Bort's knuckles and lips were taut and white.

"Waste disposal unit," he croaked.

The monitors were suddenly flashing, as TodLab LXI routinely ejected a second medical waste disposal container from its dark side.

The implosion devices whirred to life, and the countdown began. The fail-safe trigger screamed its warning into the command module, its sensors detected an alien life form *leaving* the station: the second waste disposal unit — *Cotlow's* — raced the outer perimeter of the implosion's range.

The Seed, still struggling to escape.

'Bort choked with laughter.

"The implosion device, Cotlow, you asshole — its detonation will suck the pod back into its vortex! Die, hellspawn, die — !"

'Bort's eyes slid from the damned unit containing Cotlow and the Seed to the unit the station had jettisoned seconds before by his own hand:

Rat.

Her escape route paralleled Cotlow's, both silvery orbs spinning away from the station like mercurial globes.

'Bort's eyes burned with tears.

She would die in fire, die in nothingness, the oblivion her father had condemned her to since birth. She was right: life held nothing but pain and fear and darkness, all-consuming darkness —

Infinitesimal against the girth of the station, four lights flashed from the fail-safe units. The Baby Boomer blinked away its final seconds. A final glimmer, and the four implosion units would detonate.

'Bort's features darkened, tears running over creased scar tissue as he guided the command ship out of the station's orbit. The expanse of the station was cleared in seconds as the ship rushed to follow the two silver waste units.

He hoped the command ship was large enough with force fields at full capacity to block the force of the detonation, perhaps give Rat precious seconds to clear the vortex of the all-consuming implosion...

He kept his eyes fixed on the furthest of the two, for that was where his heart lay, with the devil between them.

She should clear the perimeter of the implosion, if he were fleet and massive enough. She would escape its reach.

She might...

As Shitkicker bathed laughing in geysers of acid —

— Point pitched forward trailing splintered marrow —

— Ears' white eyes stared unseeing at the last sights beheld by his many heads —

— 'Bort's howl tore at their ears until it, and all about it, was devoured by an all-consuming sun that raged, whimpered, and collapsed into nothingness.

The silver egg held her, shielded her.

Rat coiled herself in the center of the unit, nestled in its refuse-lined interior. Her breathing was shallow, barely fogging the mask that cupped her face. Her mind was lost in herself (*Sparky*), in the comforting (*daddy can't see me now*) darkness.

The oxygen reserve would last for a short time, a precious short time. Perhaps it would last until oblivion spread its arms and welcomed her home.

Perhaps it could afford the life span of a kitten, or a boy, or that of a dream.

She sighed, and resigned herself for the first time to life — however brief — without fear.

The silver egg would protect her.

Nestled in the darkness and crazy quilt mash of glass, metal, plastic, and disposed flesh, Cotlow girded himself for the shock wave. But there was nothing: no jolt, no heat, no tugging at his body as the waste unit hurtled through the void, long freed of the station's orbit and the implosion's vortex.

Cotlow's head was leaking, crimson droplets wavering from his ragged hair, tainted by the rich violet of the stimulants that still kept him awake.

His shoulder was pulped, but there was no pain. The pain throbbed in his temples, from the spastic rustling of the new Queen in his belly, and the grinding of Richards' shoes against his head wound. Even in death, the man was an abusive nuisance.

Cotlow knew he was dying: slowly, willingly. He welcomed oblivion. He was Chosen, and would die knowing he'd fulfilled his purpose to the almighty Mother.

Perfection. It was perfection, but he'd never planned it this way. The waste disposal pod was sealed and shielded, another womb, an extension of his own. The wriggling at his chest briefly wrenched him back to the pull of meat, pain, and mortality.

The human infant struggled under his shirt, locked in Cotlow's embrace. The final gulps of air were gone, its screams finally stilled. The baby would die, denying the Queen's hive its first virgin host, but there would be others, as long as She survived.

She was the Mistress Almighty of Survival.

He was dying, but She would feed on him, on the infant's tender veal, on Richards and the edible wastes. It wasn't their usual way, but if it were the only means left to her —

Protect and Proliferate.

He had done the best he could, under the circumstances. When She was ready, when the time and place was right, She would find a way out. The hive would be born anew.

Of that he was sure, for She was the face and jaws of God, and God was Almighty.

The Queen is dead.

Long Live the Queen.